Learn to write your memoir in four weeks

A step by step guide to record the stories of your life

A Self-Study Workbook

By Jerry Waxler

Learn to write your memoir in 4 weeks by Jerry Waxler

Copyright ©2007 by Jerry Waxler, M.S.

Published by Neuralcoach Press

PO Box 99

Quakertown, PA 18951

www.neuralcoach.com

Cover Design: Ronald Dorfman

Editing: Kathryn Craft

Printed in the U.S.A.

10 9 8 7 6 5 4 3 2

ISBN 978-0-9771895-1-9

8/21/2007

Introduction

"I've looked at life from both sides now. From up and down, and still somehow, it's life's illusions I recall. I really don't know life at all." Joni Mitchell

I was 21 years old when I first shared Joni Mitchell's longing to make sense of both sides of life. I too had seen a couple of things and agreed with her that I wasn't seeing past life's illusions. So I tried to see more sides.

I earned a bachelor's degree in physics, because I thought science might teach me the secrets of the universe, and then I meditated to search for those secrets inside. I tried being poor, refusing to work because I wanted to follow the hippie way. I worked in a factory, because I thought manual labor was more "honest." I've programmed computers to diagnose and treat cancer and to guide cruise missiles, and I wrote manuals to describe software programmed by others. I went back to school when I was fifty and got a master's degree in counseling psychology, then I sat with people and listened to their deepest concerns. I overcame stage fright to talk to groups. To find my writing voice, and help other people find theirs, I wrote a book about writing. Despite all these experiences, I still have not seen life from all sides.

I have not, for instance, held a gun in battle. I have not held my own child or lost one. I am not a doctor, a Moslem, a woman, or a musician. I have never worked a farm or volunteered in the Peace Corps. To look at life from the billions of perspectives I can never own through experience, I rely on you.

When you imagine telling your story, you're like a painter in front of a blank canvas. At first images exist only inside your mind. Your job is to move these images from your mind to the blank canvas and transform them into something you can share with the world.

When you start this process, you discover that the memoir writer's palette does not contain fully formed stories. It contains only memories, and like the painter's raw material, memories are formless globs. Memory rambles. It has no plot. Memory picks and chooses. Memory whines and doesn't really care if it makes a point.

This workbook will help you turn memory into story by breaking the large assignment to "write your memoir" into smaller steps and techniques. I've used "four weeks" as an image to help you visualize putting these lessons into your own calendar. The length of time it takes you to apply these lessons will depend on your background, effort, and the size of your project.

One at a time, these lessons will take you farther along the journey. Over time, your thoughts and answers will fill a book.

1

Why tell your life story?

Perhaps you already feel motivated to write about your life. Or perhaps you're on the fence, not sure of your goal. In either case, I suggest you take a few minutes to contemplate your reasons in more detail. By moving your reasons from inside your mind onto paper, you gain several benefits.

Some activities offer quick pleasure. Say you want to have some ice cream. You find the ice cream and eat it. You've achieved the pleasure and you're done. Other pleasures take longer, and involve more steps. Writing your memoir is one of those that will not offer instant rewards. And over the period of time it takes you to write your memoir, you may have moments during which your enthusiasm needs renewal. At those times, you can pull out your list of reasons and review them. You might even buff up the list and add a few more reasons to help you stay focused on achieving your goal.

Understanding your reasons will benefit you in another way. Your deeper understanding will help you organize your memory writing. For example, if you want to reach people with a message, keep this message in mind as you craft your story. Or your desire to entertain people might result in a search for humor or excitement.

Here are some of the reasons people offer for writing about their lives.

- "Learning to tell it would give me a creative challenge."
- "I want to give my kids a window into my world."
- "I love writing, and this project will get me going."
- "I want to organize thoughts about who I am by seeing where I've been."
- "My story contains observations that could help others."
- "I want to share myself in a way that shows others who I am."
- "I want to teach or popularize some expertise I have acquired."
- "I hope to publish and make money."
- "I want to make peace with issues from my past."

Write

Borrow from this list, or add your own, and tell in your own words the reasons you want to write about your life.

2

Who is your audience?

How do you start organizing a lifetime of memories into a story? A good place to begin is to imagine telling your story to an audience. The reason is simple. The whole chain of our verbal machinery — all the way from our brain cells to our vocal chords to our vocabulary and sentence rules — is aligned to enable us to communicate. So instead of staring at a page and wondering how to fill it, apply your instinct to speak. By picturing your audience you can gain insight into what you want to say and how to say it.

Visualize these possibilities:

- Family and friends, who want to know more about you now and later.
- A special interest group with whom you share experience or knowledge.
- The general public.

As your audience emerges from the shadows, your story will be influenced by factors such as what they already know, and what they want to know.

Say, for example I want to describe the day I got on the airplane to go to college for the first time. If I was telling my friends, they already have an enormous amount of information about who I am now, so any story about the past would be placed Into that context. I have a certain image to maintain with these people, which will influence the story I tell.

Another audience might be students, their parents, and alumni of the University of Wisconsin. I could focus on details about particular university buildings and street names. They would want to take the journey with me onto campus in 1965.

The general public has different knowledge and needs. They don't know me, so when I tell them my story I must provide them with reasons to care. I must establish the emotional significance of this scene, sharing my anxiety and hopes for the future. My challenge is to let them identify with a boy crossing the threshold from childhood into the next stage in his life.

Write

Describe your audience.

Imagine you are standing in front of them, and ready to tell your tale. How do <u>you</u> feel? Warm? Eager? Distant? Describe your feelings.

Now describe the way you imagine <u>their</u> feelings. Are they eager to hear your story? If not, refine the composition of your imaginary audience. Populate it with fans. Find an audience who really wants to hear what you have to say. Now describe this audience.

3

Decide what you want to tell them

Some experiences have obvious story-power. If you were one of the people who knocked down the Berlin Wall, or you were a soldier in the Vietnam War, you might think, "There's a book here." Or if you were a police officer or worked in an emergency room where you witnessed life and death scenarios every day, you may have said, "I should write a book."

Or you may feel your life has been ordinary, and you're not sure what to write. As you further explore the hills and valleys of your life, you realize some of your transitions had emotional power. You might uncover great emotional upheaval in your divorce or your care for a parent with Alzheimer's. It may not be headline news, but writing about it will have therapeutic value for you, and offer others support and information about surviving similar situations.

In sifting through their past, here are some of the angles other writers have considered.

- As they dig into family background, they discover powerful facts that have influenced them from behind a cloak of secrecy.
- When writing about the past, they realize how different it was from the way other people grew up. What at first seemed boring turns out to be fascinating.

- Childhood anxiety about being left alone, or abused, or bullied, turns out to have resonance throughout their life story. By writing about it, things start coming out that have been forgotten for years.
- They identify mistakes made during the transition from child to adult that they either regret or in some cases have forgotten entirely. As they tell the story, they realize how powerful those events were, and begin to organize them into a sensible sequence.
- They want to share lifetime accomplishments such as career, art, family, or art.
- They want to share a segment of life they saw from inside (military wife, policeman, hippie commune, government office)

Write

Write in your notebook some ideas, as general or specific as you would like, about what you want to write.

Describe a sequence of events that you feel is particularly important for you to tell.

Pretend you sit down on an airplane. You have about an hour to tell the person next to you the story you would like to write in your memoir. What would you say? Because of your time limit, don't go too deeply into a particular scene. Try to cover the main points.

4

Choose a form

What is a memoir, anyway? No governing body controls the definition, which leaves us to make up our own rules. Basically you can write about your life any way you want. Depending on the author's purpose, a memoir might focus on just one period, or give an overview of an entire life. It could emphasize entertainment, or convey information. So instead of looking for the "right answer," consider the range of possibilities, and select the form that suits your own goals.

Memoir

A memoir is a story about your life that stays as close as possible to the facts, while using enough storytelling techniques to make it interesting enough to be read by a stranger. You might want to focus on a particular aspect of your life, or try to cover a broad range.

Essay

An essay is crafted to make some point. "God had mercy." "War is heck." "If only we took care of our environment…"

Autobiography

An autobiography provides the facts about your life. This emphasizes completion, even if it slows down the readability. For example, "My parents moved to this country in 1911. I was born in 1947..."

Historical record

You may want to provide a detailed history of a period, as seen through your eyes. It's okay to provide extensive, researched background in your memoir. The history itself can be part of the story. "The sixties as seen from the eyes of someone who was there."

Teach

If you were a stock broker or a movie director, you could show people how your world worked.

Fiction based on facts

In fiction, you can change the facts any way you want. Change your career, merge two siblings into one, switch the alcoholism from a parent to an uncle. At one extreme, your life experience may simply be a springboard for telling an entertaining story. Or on the other extreme, you may want to tell your accurate memoir, but are afraid of offending people. In either case, fiction gives you the freedom to tell your story more intimately.

Combining goals

This list of forms sounds straightforward, but in reality, memoir writers combine a variety of forms to make their own unique product. Consider the way these successful authors approached their memoir.

Ann Lamotte's "Bird by Bird" is a memoir about her writing career that also serves as an essay and teaching book about the art of writing.

Nian Cheng's "Life and Death in ShiangHai" is a memoir that is also a history book about the Cultural Revolution in China.

Alex Haley's "Roots" was a cross between a memoir, a novel, and a work of genealogy that crossed several generations. In addition to its fictional elements, it contained Haley's research into his past.

James Frey's book, "A Million Little Pieces" was sold as a memoir, then scandalized because of its fictional elements.

Many novels contain autobiographical elements mixed in with imaginary ones, and we may or may not find out from the author how to tell the difference.

Almost all memoirs contain some fictional elements, such as invented conversations and other detailed descriptions to help the reader relate to scenes.

Write

Which aspects of life writing appeal to you? Try to imagine your story in several of these forms, and write a few paragraphs about how the form might influence the way you slant your material.

5

Get past, "What if my writing hurts someone?"

Putting memories on paper exposes issues that typically remain private. Naturally, we wonder if our revelations might offend someone. There are many varieties of this fear, all the way from being afraid to say something less than flattering about your mother to revealing a secret that could end up in a court of law. Your affection for an ex-spouse might offend your current one, or a revelation about the past could scandalize your employer.

One woman was afraid to write about a dad who abandoned the family when she was a child. Her fear was that her rage and disgust would upset her mother.

Write

If you fear offending people, write about your fear. Who are they and how you might offend them? If you are too afraid to write it in your notebook, use a separate page, and destroy it afterwards.

Overcome the fear by writing

If you stop writing, you may never get to the resolution. Rather than try to work out the resolution before you start writing, set aside your concern and write about the memory as clearly as possible. You may find that the best way to overcome your fear is by writing. As you write, you gain insights, find resolutions, and become clearer about the situation. The writing itself answers the fear.

If you fear your comments may land you in court, I encourage you to either find a lawyer, or as some writers have done, wait to publish until the other person is dead. But if your fear is emotional, look for ways to wend your way through the thicket of feelings. Look for nuances, healing, fictional accounts, or other devices to help you overcome your fear and tell your story.

Fictionalize

To help face fear-based issues, try writing your story as fiction. Simply change the names or other external facts, and jump in. Give yourself permission to change even salient facts. This will reduce the potential for offense and provide an additional degree of distance to help you get to the heart of the matter. Chances are the people you are afraid of offending won't recognize themselves or may even be flattered. And you can claim it was "just fiction."

Exorcise Demons

Whether you fictionalize or stick to the facts, you might find that writing helps you exorcise demons. Take the example of childhood neglect. When you were little, you needed your parents to be your gods and protectors, and their behavior towards you was an unpardonable sin. Yet now, as you write the story, you might get a glimpse of the tragedy in their lives. You no longer feel the same way. Or you no longer need to write it with the same bitterness. The whiny anger in your draft may not seem valuable enough to include in your final version. In the final story, the truth might come out in a nuanced way that helps you find your own humanity, and gives the other person enough humanity that you no longer fear sharing it.

The woman who wrote the story about being abandoned as a child came to terms with her own anger. In her fictional account, to create a compelling story, she developed her dad as a multi-dimensional person. She saw his point of view for the first time, and was able to bring closure to her painful memories. Her fear evaporated.

In another example, an author wanted to write about his childhood. He started the chapter with a scathing indictment of his mother. One of his complaints was that his mother was intrusive. True to form, she demanded to read what he was writing. He reluctantly showed it to her. Much to his surprise, this triggered a deep, genuine communication between them that resulted in more intimacy, not less.

Deconstruct your fear

Fears are usually based on predictions, not facts. If you think the terrifying results will take place after you write your account, you are projecting your thoughts far into the future. You haven't even written your memoir yet. The other basis for the fear is mind reading. You are assuming you understand the other person's mind. You could be wrong. The person may feel differently or not even care about your account. Or you may tell the story in nuances that leave the other person feeling whole. Don't let fear create imaginary obstacles.

Write

What will it take for you to set aside your fear and start writing? Brainstorm, talk to counselors, or people in similar situations. Devise a plan that lets you start putting words on paper.

6

Answer "What if I remember wrong?"

When two people walk out of a room and compare notes about the lecture they both heard, they might disagree about the exact words spoken just moments earlier. The problem gets worse over time. So even though you want to tell the truth, you realize how shaky memory is. The fear of misremembering may seem so embarrassing you would rather not write anything than write something wrong.

Since we can't nail down absolute truth, no matter how hard we try, there is no answer to the question "Is it true?" And asking this question will lead you nowhere. To move forward with your writing, make peace with the notion of a best approximation.

Instead of looking for truth, look for the story. The story itself will contain a compelling logic, and it is that logic that you are trying to convey. Of course, if you want to represent your story as true, you must base on it the best version of facts you can muster.

Do the research

In addition to your memory, look for other sources of information. Go to the library and find newspapers from the period you write about. Research on the internet. To keep his memoir as close to truth as possible, Foster Winans looked up the weather report on the days of his key scenes. Draw diagrams of important scenes. Interview anyone who was there, so you can compare their statements with yours. Even though their accounts may differ from yours, their recollections may reveal new details.

Be a storyteller

When creating a scene, insert dialog to help the scene move forward and convey information between characters. Try to keep your dialog as close as possible to the way you remember the scene, even though you don't remember the exact words. You may be tempted to insert some sort of disclaimer, such as "To the best of my knowledge, she said something similar to…" That would be tedious to read, and would break up the realism of the scene. So leave these disclaimers out, and explain this approach once in the front of the book.

Do the same thing with clothing, furniture, or other details that bring realism to the scene. It's hard to describe colors in words anyway, especially colors that you saw 30 years ago. So make it up. Have fun. Give yourself permission to write a readable story.

Write:

Remember a conversation you had with someone several weeks ago. Without writing any disclaimers like "to the best of my recollection," describe the other person's clothes. Report exactly what was said.

Now take a more creative approach. Write it with more storytelling flair. Add some drama or details.

7

Overcome "I'm not a good writer."

Many people are afraid to tell their story because they don't feel qualified. If this is one reason you have not written your memoir, think about your concerns in more detail.

Set aside grammar and spelling

Grammar and spelling ought to be technical issues. However, for most of us, they are loaded with powerful emotions. These skills were instilled in us when we were young and impressionable, and our technical shortcomings may still carry the stigma of classroom humiliation. The real shame is burying your life story beneath this fear.

Improve writing technique

Writing, like any skill, improves with learning and practice. You will only improve through trying. And the good news is that you already know how to learn. Throughout your life you have gone from novice to expert in a variety of skills, from tying shoelaces, to driving a car, to learning a sport. We keep learning through life. Improving your writing skills is simply another step along that journey.

To improve your writing, seek instruction. Here are some of the methods available to aspiring writers:

- Read about writing.

- Join writing groups; attend continuing education classes, workshops, and conferences.
- Hire a guide or editor.
- Practice.

Write

What other skills have you learned? (sewing, computers, sports, musical instrument)

What was your skill level when you first started?

How long did it take to become proficient?

What did you do to go from unskilled to skilled?

Encourage yourself

Imagine yourself encouraging a friend or child to learn something valuable. You explain that it's harder at the beginning. That learning is incremental. That they should find strength in small victories and not to overemphasize defeats. Apply this same tact with yourself. Speak to yourself as if you were someone you love and respect. What would you tell yourself to help you move towards your goal?

Absorb praise

If someone praises you, do you ever think, "He's just saying that?" Dismissing praise is one way to perpetuate a feeling of worthlessness. If you want to improve your opinion of yourself, open up and absorb praise. When someone offers you a compliment, slow down. Take time to thank the person and think about what they said from a trusting point of view. Get more details. When you pay attention to praise, you find out what you are doing right, and this guides you towards improved quality.

Write

List several things you can do in the coming year to get beyond the "I can't write" block.

8

Organize messy memories

Memories pop through our mind in a random order. I can remember a snip from my childhood, walking to elementary school. It could have taken place almost any school day within those six years. Then I see a pile of fallen leaves, so that memory takes place in autumn. In another snip, I reach up to the flowers growing through the schoolyard fence and pull off a honeysuckle. That must have been spring. In my next memory I'm riding my bike around the neighborhood. I can feel the heat, so that would have been in summer. In memory, time flips and interleaves like the shards of colored glass in a kaleidoscope.

Write

Think of a location and action from three different years of your life. Notice how you can skip back and forth from one time to the next, effortlessly and instantaneously. Read on for effective techniques that will help you organize your memories.

Scenes hang together

This property of memories, to jump and weave, makes them fundamentally different from life. In life, events move one after the other in sequence. So when I remember an event, it obeys the randomness of memories. But once I'm inside the scene, events unfold in order. When I enter a scene of walking to school, I see myself closing the front door behind me, walking down the concrete stairs, holding onto the railing. Then I turn left past our curbside maple tree and proceed past the row of parked cars on my right and lawns on my left. Telling events in sequence is natural in life, and it is necessary in stories.

If we tried to write our memoir in the order memories occurred to us, the reader would be unable to follow it. To write a readable piece, you must translate from the language of memory to the language of story.

The key to this translation process is to present your story in scenes. When you enter the scene, it's almost as if you popped the video recording into the player and hit the play button. This ability to enter a scene and tell it in order will be a basic building block of your memoir.

Write

Remember a particular scene. The time you missed a plane flight, for instance, or whatever event occurs to you. Even though the scene jumped at random out of the pile of memories, once you're inside the scene, describe the events. Write what happened, while staying inside the scene.

Bonus question. What year did it happen?

9

Build a framework: The Timeline

Memory can jump anywhere it wants, so to tame it you need to apply an organizing principle. I suggest a timeline. By gathering the events and positioning them in the order they occurred, you will take an important step toward translating memories into memoirs. The timeline creates an order that lets you tell the sequence and lets readers understand it.

At first this may not seem possible – you didn't keep extensive records. You're not sure when things happened. Capturing a memory might feel like trying to catch a ray of light. Every time you think you have one, it slips away. Applying a simple timeline strategy will help you put them in place. Like a pointillist painter who adds a bit here and a bit there, soon the whole picture will start to take form.

Write

List the decades of your story down the left side of a sheet of paper or word processing document. If your story takes place on a smaller timeframe, list the years. For example:

1970

1980

1990

Next to each decade, describe the main events. Where did you live, work, or go to school? Who did you live with? What major transitions took place? What are you most proud of?

Write

Insert smaller time periods on to your timeline—for example, try using five year periods—and repeat the same exercise.

Fill the timeline

Now that you have started your timeline, you can use it to organize your brainstorming. Let your memory jump where it wants, from decade to decade, across thousands of miles, forward or back. Take advantage of this wild flight by filling in the timeline. As you remember each point, place it on the line in chronological order. When I remember the name of my second grade teacher, Mrs. Moss, I put it in the timeline at the right year (1954). When I remember boarding the plane for my first trip to college (1965), I simply scroll down the page and put that into its right place.

Putting random memories into chronological order gives a new way to see your life. Like framing out a house with two by fours, the timeline creates the structure. Later you'll hang drywall, paint, and decorate.

Write

Ask additional questions. For example:

- What vacations did I take?
- Who was my go-to person?
- What pets did I own, or hobbies did I do?

Scan each period, filling in the answers in order. If you remember the exact year, or month, write that in so you can continue to sort events. Repeat this as a warmup exercise every time you sit down to write. Keep a list of questions handy, and if you think of a new question, add it the list. By expanding your list of questions, you can turn up details you had not thought about in years.

Write

Enhance your list right now by adding five more memory jogging questions.

10

Zoom in on specific periods

Students in my workshops often report that filling in the timeline provided their very first overview of the events that unfolded in their lives. Looking across the span of time gives you a structured way to see which events happened before others, which were closer to others, which were similar to others.

From this overview, you will notice high intensity periods that stand out from the rest. Perhaps these dramatic moments motivated you to write your memoir in the first place. Or perhaps you are just now seeing their importance in the overall story of your life.

Write

What particular episodes emerge from your life span, that you want to focus on? You don't need to craft a complete story yet. You are still gathering and organizing the facts.

Zoom in on interesting times

When you identify areas of particular importance, the experiences themselves will dictate a timeframe. For example, if you were evacuated from your house to avoid an oncoming hurricane, instead of measuring time in years, you may need to focus on hours. Shift your focus down to the appropriate time frame for this experience and ask questions that bring you into those events. For example, when you entered the evacuation shelter:

- What was it like trying to fall asleep?
- Who did you meet?
- Where did you get information?
- What happened when the emergency was over?

Write

Select a particular period of interest. Shift the scale of your timeline to match the unfolding events during this period. Ask questions that will evoke more memories during that period.

11

Reveal information by association

When we remember our lives, we enter one moment in time. As we review it, something else attracts our attention and we leap off again into another time and place. It's like rustling around in a pile, pulling something out, throwing it back, and rustling around again. But once you learn how to work the system, you can steer more productively, taking advantage of the way one memory links to others.

Instead of letting the details slip past, slow down and examine the specific scene you have jumped into. Take out your pad and take notes. What happened? Who was there? Report how things looked, felt, and sounded. By using your curiosity and powers of observation, you can enter the scene further, move in interesting directions, and reveal facts you had not thought about for decades.

For example, it's easy for me to get a hazy picture of my walk to elementary school. I'd like to learn more, so I'll see what happens when I walk a little further. Hmmm. Now I see that after school, I walked in the opposite direction from my house, towards religious study class. I had not thought about it for years, and can't remember a single thing about it. I jump into my memory and continue the walk. I pass a bakery on Ogontz Avenue and look in the window, and feel the pangs of desire. I pull open the heavy glass door and smell aromas of pastries and bread, but I have eyes only for the cookies, each about six inches in diameter, bigger, thicker, and fresher than any cookie I can get at home. I lean forward for a closer look, trying to decide which flavor I want, the chocolate ones with a dark brown crust, or the butter ones with sugar on top. The woman behind the counter is serving another customer and I hear the chatter of a bread slicer. When it's my turn, I order two cookies, one of each kind. I hand over my money, and the clerk hands me a white paper bag. As I walk out, I reach in, pull one out and take a bite. Now I'm ready to finish my walk.

Memories become more and more real as you see them, touch them, hear them, smell them, taste them. Suppose I want to remember the upstairs hall in my childhood home, but it seems invisible. Then I remember there is large phone on the wall in the hallway closet. I fix my attention on that phone. It's some sort of heavy black composite material. I place it to my ear, and that reminds me that if I wanted privacy, I could lean tightly against the linen shelves and pull the door closed behind me. In the dark, I can smell the fresh linen and can feel the clean sheets. Why did I want privacy? Oh right. I was talking to a girl who called me, and I felt awkward and told her I didn't think I could see her again, which was weird because I liked her, but I was just so shy. Then my heart starts pounding with shyness, and I see myself driving the car the night I went on a date with her.

Write

Peer more closely into a snippet of memory. Touch and smell things. Describe visual details. Use the magic of association to remember more.

12

Free-write scenes

Many people believe that writing must be perfect on the first draft. This idea will poison your motivation. First, it makes you look at imperfect drafts as a sign of "bad writing." Second, to follow the myth, you must obsess on each word while you are writing it. Rewriting and judging your writing while you are trying to get words on paper interferes with your flow, turns writing into drudgery, and may ultimately stop you altogether. If you are ever going to finish your memoir, you need to break out of perfect first drafts.

The method for moving to the next step is called free-writing. When you free-write, the main rule is "don't stop." If you can't think of a word, use any word that comes to mind and just keep going. If you feel clumsy about this process and want to review a word you just wrote, let yourself feel clumsy and keep writing.

Your inner censor has been poking its nose into your writing for so long you may not know how to stop it. It takes practice. You'll get used to it, and once you've learned to free-write, you'll be able to dash out sentences, paragraphs, and scenes as fast as you can write.

First draft writing is not perfect

Your first-draft writing won't be perfect. It may not even be close. Some of your writing may sound like the work of a child, or so awkward you want to burn it. Everyone who writes faces shoddy first drafts. You'll take care of these problems later, when you edit.

> *Tip: After you free-write chunks of your memoir, don't show them to anyone. You wouldn't roll out of bed and walk into a business meeting. First you brush your teeth and get dressed. Draft writing needs to be edited before it's ready for the public.*

Practice free-writing

To gain the knack of writing first drafts, practice the "pure" form of free-writing as an exercise. Free-writing, as a "pure" exercise, expands your writing energy, allowing you to ramble and say whatever comes to mind. This is great for journaling, for self-discovery, and for practice at soothing the inner censor. It doesn't need to have shape. It doesn't need to mean anything. You can throw it away afterwards. The point is not to generate great writing. The point is to calm your inner critic, and gain the knack of moving words easily from mind to paper.

Write

You may enjoy the tactile sensation of writing in long hand in a blank book, or you may prefer an empty document on your computer. It's up to you. Select whichever medium lets you feel relaxed and open. Pick any topic—say, what you did the day before, or what you dreamt the night before. Then start writing, following the central rule, "Don't stop." Don't erase. Don't go back. Don't debate. Just keep writing.

13

Move towards your goal

While free-writing lets you rapidly pour words from your mind onto paper, this completely unstructured approach may not seem to lead anywhere. The next step is to maintain the freedom while at the same time shaping your writing in a form that makes sense to readers.

Choose a spot. Then jump in.

Imagine you're walking along a stream and you want to see something on the other side. To find a place to cross, you stop looking at the opposing bank and start looking at the stream. You think you see a path, so you jump on the first rock. Once you start leaping, your feet take over. Before you even land on one rock, you are already lining up the next one. You get to the other side, approximately where you aimed, approximately along the path you had visualized, but with a few surprises along the way. It was fun, liberating, and got you where you wanted to go.

Direct your free-writing the same way. As you consider the facts around a particular period, a scene attracts your attention. Emotions from the scene come into focus, and you start feeling them. Once you align your memory with this scene, jump in. One event reveals another. You'll find yourself describing things you didn't remember. Write them, and move to the next, like leaping across the moments. This sense of immediacy will help you enter and stay inside the scene.

By letting yourself enter the scene, the way you might have when you first experienced it, you'll be able to feel it, and so will your reader. Tell the reader what you see, hear, smell, taste, and touch. These are the "rocks" that let the reader step across the stream from your experience to theirs.

Once you're inside the scene, keep moving

Because memory moves randomly, it's easy to pop out of the scene you are writing. Say you are writing about something that happened twenty years ago, and feel tempted to insert an observation about the scene that you just thought of. "Oh," you write. "Now I see why that happened."

In one sense it looks like your comment contributes energy to the scene. Your observation could offer the reader interesting insights into your life. But in another sense you are stealing energy away from the scene. That observation took place today at your writing desk. Even though you don't realize it, your comment reminds the reader you are sitting at a desk instead of acting inside the scene.

For now, since this is free-writing, don't stop to argue with yourself about whether or not this observation really belongs here. Such debates will slow you down and disrupt your connection with the scene. There will be plenty of time later to work out these details while you are editing. For now, let it go and keep moving. Keep the inner critic as quiet as possible. You can make the best use of these insights by ignoring them while you are writing. The longer you stay inside the scene, the more you'll understand.

Later, when you are reviewing your free-writing, you can consider these observations. As an observer now, you are in a position to learn so much more about your life than when you were living it.

Say you are writing a scene in the kitchen, and you mention that the table was replaced several years later. That's not in the scene, and there's no reason to keep it there. But since it popped out during your free-writing, perhaps it has some meaning. Instead of arguing about whether it's in or out, keep writing inside the scene. You notice the table leg is rickety and you feel annoyed that your parents wouldn't fix it. Later when you read your draft, it dawns on you that the reason they didn't replace the table was because they didn't have the money, but they never talked about money. Your free-writing helped reveal a deeper insight into your relationship with your parents, and their relationship with money.

Write

Use free-writing to pour out a first draft, but instead of writing about anything that comes to mind, First put yourself into a scene. Once you are inside the scene, start free-writing, while obeying the fundamental free-writing rule. "Don't stop."

14

Edit scenes to keep readers in

Because first drafts are only approximations of what you intended, a substantial amount of the effort of good writing goes into good editing. Not all of us learned to edit when in school, where the emphasis was often on the end result of good writing, rather than showing us the steps to achieve it. So now, to write well, you must learn to edit.

To teach yourself to edit, keep in mind your primary goal – make sure your writing says what you meant. The challenge is that it's difficult to read your own writing objectively. To gain more insight into what it would sound like to others, read it aloud. Or set it aside and read it a day or two later. Or join a critique group to find out if your meaning comes through to other people.

I don't recommend you get too caught up in technical issues like spelling and grammar at this stage. You're not going to suddenly become a grammar or spelling expert. Tell a compelling story. The mechanics of your writing can be fixed later.

A story does more than simply convey information in technically correct language. It also must keep the reader inside the scene. In the next section, I'll offer specific tips for making the scene more immediate. In this section I want to emphasize that the best way to keep the reader inside the scene is for you as writer to stay inside of it. Avoid reminding the reader that you are writing. Phrases like "I remember now" or "I learned later" break the reader's concentration. If such phrases slipped in during free-writing, remove them when you edit.

Here is an example of a drafted scene, complete with errors and anything else that happened to come out while I was writing:

> *"When I stood out in the driveway, washing the Studebaker. Dipping into the bucket with that big sponge. And then drying it with a chamois (pronounced sham-ee) it was so soft. And the bucket made me think of something clean. Like I was doing something worthwhile. Cleaning that car made me feel good about myself. Of course, having my first car gave me power. But it was also a lovely gift from my father. He had got it from my aunt, who used it to drive all over the country.*
>
> *(ah-ha. I remember now my mom tells about how dad's father gave him a car at the wedding. No wonder dad years later gave me a car, even though he probably couldn't afford it. He was passing it on. Good going dad.)"*

This draft is sloppy and violates all kinds of rules about writing scenes. So after I've written it, I go back and edit it. In addition to fixing up the sentences and making sure they flow in sequence, here are some rules to keep the reader inside the scene:

- Maintain point of view by staying inside the scene.
- Don't flash forward into the future.

- Remove phrases like "I remember" or "I could hear" that remind the reader you are writing today.
- Avoid turning background into lengthy descriptions that would break up the scene. Instead use tiny flashbacks or add dialog to let people talk about what happened before.

Here is the same snippet after editing.

> "I stood out in the alley behind my house and poured a cap full of cleaning solution into the bucket of water. That was the best cleaner I could find, after examining every single auto cleaner at the auto-part store. I dipped the large "turtle" sponge into the bucket, and then smacked it onto the Studebaker and rubbed in a circular motion. Oops. One of the small ventilation windows wasn't shut all the way. I pulled the window and turned the latch, smiling at the state decals Aunt Florence had applied to the windows. "She drove this thing all over the country. Now it's mine. My first car," I thought. I turned on the hose and the mist caught the sunlight and created tiny rainbows. Then I threw the hard chamois cloth into the water to soften it, wrung it out, and caressed the surface until it was dry."

What about that bit where I remembered my grandfather giving my dad a car, and now my dad is giving me one? That thought was evoked by the scene, but it's not in the scene. The boy washing the car didn't think of it then. I'm thinking of it while I'm writing. By making an observation about the scene, I break the reader out of the time frame. And yet it's a compelling point that may be interesting to work with later. When I'm ready to look for the emotion inside the scene, I can review this point more closely.

15

Edit more

In real life, actions play out one after the other. We walk into a room, turn on the television, and sit on the couch. Someone else walks into the room. We say "hello." It's a sequence. But there is a lot more going on than just a list of actions.

A scene is rarely so simple that only one thing is happening at a time. If the television is playing, then at least two things are happening. And while people walk and talk, they are also thinking and feeling. How you weave together the warp and woof of simultaneous actions will rely not on a formula, but on your evolving craft. Here are a few guidelines to create a scene that makes sense to the reader.

Backdrop

Let the reader know what the setting looks like. Remember, unless you tell them about it, they can't see it. But you can't just stop mid-action to paint a backdrop. You need to artfully weave descriptions into the action.

Emotion

What were people feeling? You can describe feelings by describing actions. If you want me to know that you were tired, describe yourself sinking into the sofa and closing your eyes. If you were angry, smack something down on the table.

Write

In your scene, put in some action or physical description that will let the reader see the emotion.

Dialog

Dialog provides an excellent story element, because it portrays the actions of the speakers, and it also conveys information through their words. Instead of *I was angry,* write: *I felt my face heat up and said, "How dare you show up so late? You know how important that meeting was to me."*

Write

Return to your scene, and instead of telling about an event, let the dialog describe it.

Sensory description

As you sit down on the sofa, help the reader see and feel what happened. Describe the lumpy sensation of the blanket that is draped over the holes in the upholstery, and reach down and pull out an empty soda can. If your fingers are sticky afterwards, the reader will feel it with you. Instead of "it was a bad neighborhood," look out the window and see an abandoned car. By sharing sights, sounds, smells, touches, and tastes, you evoke images that will help the reader participate in your experience.

Write

Go through your scene, and add a detail of something you can see, touch, feel, taste, or smell.

16

Sleuth for emotional power in scenes

Suppose you are writing about a discussion with your "ex" that got out of control. To make a point, you smashed a valuable glass sculpture against the wall. Action like this engages your readers far more intimately than a statement, "I was angry." But while explosive anger is relatively easy to show, the human condition is filled with subtler emotions that do not necessarily result in external action. Disappointment, yearning, ambition — these are the emotions that make us human, and showing them will give your reader a window into the heart of your character. But how do you set up scenes that reveal these subtle emotions?

Conveying emotions, even subtle ones, turns out to be relatively easy in memoirs, once you learn the technique. The scenes you write will set up the emotional interplay for you.

At first glance, a scene you've written may seem to contain no particular significance. But look inside it. What are the characters feeling about each other? Listen to their tone of voice. Look at their body language. What does that indicate about the emotions they are feeling? Even though this scene seemed to occur in your mind randomly, you can find out more about it by asking why your mind offered up this particular scene. When you look more closely, you will often find nuances of underlying intensity staring at you from inside your scene. Your scene writing has delivered a vehicle for conveying a particular set of emotions in your life.

For example, look at the scene when I was washing the old Studebaker. This is not an exciting scene. It's just about a kid out in the driveway dipping a sponge into a bucket. But once I start looking, I find emotional themes within it. For example, I can see how proud I was washing that car. That's a stark contrast to what I usually felt back then. This is the same driveway where I was an utter failure as a neighborhood athlete, always the last to be picked for any team.

Another emotional insight popped into my mind. When dad gave me that car I figured he did so because he was my father and I needed a car. Reading back over this scene I notice emotional nuances. I suddenly make a connection with the story my mother used to tell about their wedding day, when dad's dad announced he was giving the newlyweds a car. The way she told it, it sounded rather pompous. But now that it's <u>my</u> father giving <u>me</u> a car, I realize how intimate and generous it is. It becomes a symbol of a father's connection with his son.

Out of this ordinary scene lumber two big emotional themes. One was my lack of athleticism, a trauma when I was a young man. The other is a clue to my relationship with my father, and his relationship with his father. When you look within your own scenes, you will harvest emotional themes that become available to you as a storyteller.

- The emotion in a scene shows you how it fits into the bigger picture.

- Look for similar emotions elsewhere in the story and link them together.
- Showing your emotion makes you more accessible to the reader.

   Tip: During the writing, stay inside the scene. That's where you need to be. But after you've written, try to understand what emotions drove you and the other characters in it.

To help you understand the emotions, ask questions. Suppose you wrote a scene in which your father gets agitated and starts yelling at you, and you feel helpless. After you write the scene, you look around for a place to hide, or an excuse to go outside and play.

Q: What did you want?

A: To please him, but it was not possible to please him.

Q: How did you deal with it?

A: Escaped into fantasy.

Q: What did he want?

A: He was drunk. He barely knew what he wanted.

Once you've discerned these emotions, they can help guide your story. Say you are writing a scene later in your adult life in which you are struggling to please your boss but never sure what he wants. You could use this earlier scene to help explain to the reader (and yourself!) why you had such conflicted feelings about authority.

Emotions in scenes create patterns and links

The external scene is told using external things, like sunlight and a bucket of soapy water. But inside the action there is another dimension playing out. The emotional pressure within the scene lets the reader feel what you felt. By getting in touch with this dimension you change the external actions into a vibrant connection between you and your reader.

Write

Pick a scene that you have written. Look at it more carefully. Ask questions about it:

Who did you want to please?

Who did you fear displeasing?

Who do you wish was there, but wasn't?

Now that you have seen more of life, what would you tell your younger self that might have helped you cope or steer in this situation?

Consider the emotions you are finding in your scene. How did those same emotions come up in other situations in your life?

17

Understand the stirring of emotion

As you tell your story, you will naturally arouse emotions that resonate today. Keep the pleasant ones handy to help you raise your spirits when you need them. The unpleasant ones, of course, are less fun. But they, too, offer potential value. By integrating them into your story, you can add energy to your life journey. However, if you get swept up too deeply into negative emotions, it may stop you from writing. So you need to find your way through these emotions and keep writing. In fact, the act of writing itself will help you cope. Here are some of the emotions you may experience, and suggestions for dealing with them.

Anxiety

Anxiety is nature's way of getting you to pay attention. If you are walking in a jungle and you approach a tree in which you once saw a lion, you feel anxiety. That emotion acts as a warning to help you steer clear. The problem with anxiety is that it's seldom accompanied by specific information to help us understand the danger or what to do about it. The reason anxiety is so vague is that nature designed it that way. If this tree looks anything even remotely similar to the tree where the lion was hiding, you are <u>supposed</u> to feel edgy. I'm sure this instinct saved many lives in the jungle.

Today, even though we are not walking through a jungle, our mental machinery continues to generate warnings about possible dangers, with only vague hints at the cause. By writing our memoirs we gain specific information about the lions that scared us in the first place. For example, you might remember a time when a teacher humiliated you in front of the class. You were small and vulnerable and may have felt devastated. You may even feel humiliated now when you remember it. But now, you have valuable information about the original experience that lets you see through the anxiety and transform your assailant from a lion back into a crabby teacher. She was having a bad day. The children were just trying to figure out how to be good people. It's over. It was one moment in time. Let your adult mind change it from a scary warning into an interesting story.

Write

If you feel anxious about some of your memories, describe the feeling of anxiety. Talk about what the dangers were. Brainstorm ways you can overcome this sense of danger.

Helplessness

When we were little, we depended on caregivers for protection and support. So memories from those times often awaken a sense of vulnerability. Perhaps you were made to feel helpless by a raging parent, or a natural disaster, or divorced parents, or getting lost, or a babysitter who insisted on watching a horror movie.

But it turns out that even seemingly harmless childhood experiences can arouse strong feelings. When I was little, my house of worship seemed intimidating, as did my grandparents' home. There were no shocking events that took place at these places. Instead, I suspect the anxiety was based on the realization that my parents, who were the gods at home, had to answer to a higher authority. It made my own world seem a little smaller and made me feel a little more helpless.

One place most of us experienced helplessness was when we learned how to write. Our parents desperately wanted us to learn how to be competent adults, so they shipped us off to school and granted teachers the responsibility to teach us how to communicate. Unfortunately, there is an enormous power imbalance between small children and authoritative teachers. Their corrections, grades, and criticisms left many of us feeling vulnerable for the rest of our lives about our competence as writers. You may feel such a sense of powerlessness when trying to write your memoir.

Write

What memories make you feel helpless?

Write any memories about your writing being criticized by teachers or caregivers, and how those comments make you feel now.

Flashbacks

If you experienced violent abuse or war, you may feel surges of trauma washing over you in flashbacks. Flashbacks make you feel that you are in a life and death struggle, and so it may seem counterintuitive and even dangerous to venture into telling a story about them. However, if you step carefully, avoiding land-mines so to speak, you may be able to reclaim some of your poise. Move away from your pain and look for safe, healthy, even pleasurable memories nearby. Or gain geographic distance and look for places and activities that brought you a sense of balance. By gaining solid ground in nearby memories, skip out of the flashback onto parts of the story over which you feel more safety and control.

Write

When a fire destroyed thousands of acres in Yellowstone National Park, the photos showed destroyed trees and charred, barren land. The wildflowers and saplings that poked through the blackness the following year offered a symbol of hope. In a sense, the fire was the beginning of an uplifting story. If you are disturbed by a dark period in your life, follow the same model. Start your story with the first signs of flowers emerging from the damaged soil, and tell about the rebirth that occurred in the following years.

Fear of offending

Fear of offending, like any other uncomfortable emotion, can have roots that run deep into our psyche. We are under pressure to be seen as "nice" and so we often resist complaining about people even if we believe our complaints are justified. And if it's our parents we're concerned about, this raises an added dimension. Our emotional connection with our parents is enormous, and fear of offending them can feel like a life and death struggle.

Write

Take a closer look at your fear of hurting someone in your memoir, and write an exaggerated story of what they might do to you. Play at your fear *ad nauseum* and see if you can defeat it with humor.

18

Dive into forgetfulness

Suppose you were jilted or betrayed by a lover. When it first happened you were miserable. You wanted to move on, but your search for the next step was done at the worst time. You had to look for solutions to the pain <u>while you were still in the pain</u>. You did not have the luxury of being able to step back and puzzle through the most effective way to handle the situation.

Forgetting is a valuable tool. We need to distance ourselves from the power of events, so we can get our mind back on track, and get on with our lives. The drawback to forgetting is that it robs us of the information and the conscious attention we rely upon to solve problems. Our lives have changed, but we have not integrated events into our story. Later, we find we are unable to clearly speak about this period. It is too fraught with emotion, and seems unexplainable.

Many memories may be hidden in such profound forgetfulness it's as if they never happened. Rape, for instance, or other violence against our body. Rejection from an institution we desperately wanted to enter. Abandonment by a parent. Social upheaval and natural disaster. But even though we have disengaged ourselves from these events, they have left a mark. Our bad feelings about such events may continue to spill into our mood years later, and even plunge us into a disturbing state of mind. We may end up with vague and pervasive bad feelings about ourselves or life.

So what can we do now that we are trying to describe these events in our memoir? We can look back – not to wallow in the original emotions, or the regrets at our way of handling it. But to review those times of transition so we can update our understanding about them. Out of the fog of forgetfulness we construct a conscious understanding that can help us grapple with our demons, and untangle the mess that has been hiding in the background for years. Telling the story can help us break loose from stagnation, undo self-defeating attitudes, and free us so we can move forward.

Write

If there is an old chapter of your life that is shrouded in vague regrets and recriminations, look at it as an opportunity for rewriting. Starting with the basic facts that you find troubling, create a story with a happy resolution. Sometimes describing the details helps you find completion. Other times, altering the details to suit your imagination can help you integrate those events. Whether you use truth or imagination, let the story help you find completeness. If it's too sensitive to show anyone, feel free to destroy it. Rewrite your ending as often as you like, until you find one that leaves you feeling better and empowers you to own this part of your life.

19

Manipulate emotional distance

Some memories may arouse emotions so upsetting that you find it difficult to continue. Such overwhelming emotions are not limited to painful ones. Consider, for example, high school athletes who are haunted for life by the night their peers gave them a standing ovation. Nothing else ever came close, and now, rather than a source of pleasure, it generates confusion.

To write effectively about disturbing times in your life you need to strike a good balance. Share raw feelings while at the same time maintaining enough distance that you don't feel like you're drowning in your own memories. Here are several techniques that can help you find this balance:

- Change the name of the main character and write in third person.
- Write as if you were a less interested person who happened to stop by, like a delivery man or a neighbor.
- Loosen the rigid demands of "truth" and change facts to increase your privacy and emotional safety. Over time, you may find that the memories lose their sting, and you can look for ways to portray them while maintaining your emotional balance.
- Focus on observable facts such as the color of the wall or the weather. If you were in a car crash,

what model of car was involved? If you flubbed your lines in a play, what was the name of the play, who wrote it, what was the name of the director, and how many people were in the audience? Facts will make the scene more accessible to the reader, and at the same time will help you stay grounded.

- Reduce the emotional impact of a scene by modifying the way you visualize it. Imagine you are watching it on a small, black and white television, or that you are watching it through a bulletproof observation glass.

Write

Consider a highly charged moment that haunts you. Describe it distantly and generally.

Now write about this moment using one or more of the techniques described above. Try as many of these techniques as you want. If the moment you first choose is too intense, practice on a different one.

20

Become an interesting protagonist

When we read stories, the crucial thing that keeps us turning the page is our interest in the protagonist. To stay involved, we <u>must</u> care about what happens to this person. In a memoir, this person is you! So how will you draw readers to your main character and keep them interested? Before you answer that question, consider the difference between real life and stories. In real life, we want to dress well, and be as courteous as possible to convince strangers that we are decent people. In stories, we expose ourselves to readers in a more intimate way. Since we're not perfect, they will see us with a variety of characteristics, some good, some not so good. How do we earn their interest so they'll keep turning pages despite our flaws?

Storytellers use a few classic strategies to keep readers fascinated with characters. You can offer the reader one or more of these ways to feel engaged with you.

- You an expert, someone readers can admire. Use your expertise or excellence to show readers you are competent and convince them your life is worth following.
- You are an underdog or victim, someone readers sympathize with. Use your vulnerability as a way to draw in the reader. The subtle dilemma here is that

if you look too helpless, and never do anything of your own, you risk alienating the reader. The reader wants to know what resources you developed, what avenues you tried.

- You have a raging desire to which readers can relate, such as rescuing a kidnapped daughter, or stopping a villain. The desire of the protagonist is one of the most powerful forces of the story. Select a theme that shows your powerful drive to achieve your goal.

- You need to learn a lesson. While you may want to portray yourself as a nice person, you can also gain the reader's attention by showing yourself making the same mistakes, while ignoring advice from others. This increases tension, and even fascination, as the reader waits expectantly for you to wake up and realize your mistakes, or get what's coming to you.

Write

In the story you want to tell, what will make your reader interested in your situation? Put yourself in your reader's shoes. If you were reading this book, what emotions would keep you interested enough in the protagonist to keep you turning the page?

21

Develop your protagonist's character arc

Most stories grab our attention with external events. The hero stops the terrorist or solves the crime or gets married. But a good story also grabs the reader's attention on a subtler dimension. Just as readers stay engaged so they can find out how the action unfolds, they also wonder how the events affect the main character's inner life.

This development of the protagonist is known as the "character arc." To engage the reader in your story, find the line along which you changed. This arc propels the story and gives you another structural element to follow from beginning to end. It also may provide insights that help you understand your own journey.

To find a character arc in your story, consider the various stories you enjoy. What changes in the protagonist have kept you engaged from beginning to end?

- The main character makes a big mistake or has a big problem. We'll want to know how he or she sorts it out, and recovers from this wrong turn and make things right.
- The character who doesn't learn can also keep us turning pages. If you don't learn a lesson, what sort of payback resulted?

- At first, the protagonist struggles mightily to achieve an externally gratifying objective. By the end, the protagonist recognizes that the real satisfaction comes from a more sublime reward.
- The protagonist learns a lesson about the goodness of the world, for example, that love is more powerful than selfishness, or a lesson about the badness of the world and how to cope with it in an effective way.

Write

Think of a few stories you enjoyed, and explain in a sentence or paragraph how the protagonist changed from the beginning to the end.

Consider your own story. How did you change from the beginning to the end? There is no one "right" answer to this question. You can experiment until you find a compelling arc that will help readers identify with you as you progress through the story.

22

Maintain your contract with the reader

Old television shows used a microphone lowered on a long boom, so it would hover out of sight of the camera. I became aware of this technical detail when the camera would accidentally catch a glimpse of the microphone. Suddenly, instead of watching a married couple sitting in their living room, I was watching two actors sitting on props. The trance of the story was interrupted. Similarly, to keep people in your story, keep the microphone out of sight. Avoid doing things that remind the reader of your writing. To keep the writing "off camera," keep in mind these three Point Of View (POV) techniques.

- Stay inside one mind at a time.
- Stay in one period at a time.
- Show the reader where you are.

Stay inside one mind

Once you have established your point of view, the reader knows whose mind he is in. It's so easy for the writer to slip and report the thoughts in a different character's mind! This slip is a typical glitch in first draft writing, when you are just trying to get the whole thing on paper. When you re-read, you may notice thoughts that would only be known by a different character. Edit these out, so you can stay inside one mind at a time. With care, it's possible to use more than one point of view, but rarely within one scene and never within one paragraph. If you are writing a memoir about a long courtship, you could switch back and forth between you and your partner. But you need to learn the signals and techniques that keep the reader oriented and comfortable.

Stay inside one time

Because we're so accustomed to memories that jump from time to time, it's tempting to pepper a scene with observations about what happened before or what happened later, but the more flashbacks and flash forwards you use, the harder the reader has to work. Of course, storytelling does often give information from different times. But it must be done consciously. The best time to shift is at a chapter break, but even then, be sure to give the reader clear clues about the place and time. Unless you are a polished storyteller, you will probably make the reader's job easiest by telling events as close to their sequential order as possible.

Stay inside one place

You help keep the reader grounded by maintaining a clear connection with your external physical scene. By showing readers what's on the wall, what clothes you are wearing, what the weather is like, you will keep them grounded in your point of view.

Write

Review your memoir writing, and note every time you shift one of these POV features.

23

Orient the reader to your world

Backdrops are the canvas on which your life was painted. They provide context for the scenes so the reader can feel that there is a room, a town, and a world surrounding you. This backdrop might at first not seem important to you. When you experienced intense moments, such as the time you proposed marriage, your feelings seem to be the most important element of the scene. But readers can't see feelings. To let them see that scene, show them the surroundings. If your proposal took place in a restaurant, the loud conversations at a nearby table and the waiter asking for your order not only provide a visual impression but also heighten a sense of expectation.

Each individual scene is relatively easy to describe. First you describe the restaurant. Then when you break the news to the in-laws, you can show a living room in a suburb. But a story doesn't consist of isolated scenes. They all tie together. By building a coherent, interesting world, you tie together your experience so the reader can understand the whole thing. So just as you looked for a way to make the events of your life tie together into a story, plan out how you will offer an interesting and coherent backdrop.

For example, in the New York Times bestselling memoir, "Trading Secrets," about scandal in the stock market, R. Foster Winans draws us into scenes in the usual way, showing people and places. But to provide a compelling story that carries us from beginning to end, he gives an insider's glimpse into how stock market traders spend their day, and how the management team at the Wall Street Journal makes decisions. From individual scenes, to chapters, to the entire story, he provides enough sense of his world that readers can feel part of it.

In your recollection, tell us about your world, so we'll know you better, too. For example, as a child, I was at religious school, and out of that tinny brown speaker above the door came President Kennedy's announcement that we were blockading Cuba. Later I sat alone in my living room listening to a plane flying overhead, wondering if it could drop a nuclear bomb. The Cold War helps me weave a tale and gives you another way to see me.

A tale of immigrating from Cuba shows the interaction with the government bureaucracy, and lets us see the challenge of adapting to a new culture within the immigrant community. Writing about life along a Texas border, a memoir paints a picture of its relentless dust, dual culture, and limited options. This slice of life gives the reader an insider look at the border town sub-culture. If you were in a war, tell about the hierarchy of grunts and officers. Don't assume readers know the lingo. Inform them. While the reader learns about you, they are also learning more about your world. It keeps them turning pages and bonds you with them.

Writes

What sort of scenery, backdrop, or world events will you share with the reader? For example, career, history, culture, family, geography, music, hobby, arts, etc.

What parts of life do you see from inside? For example, consider what it would be like to tell about your particular family dynamics, your career, geography, working in a hospital or ambulance.

24

Keep the reader in suspense

Suspense is the feeling in a story that keeps the reader wondering what is going to happen next. It's like the tension on a sling shot. Once you pull it back, you feel primed and incomplete until the shot is released. Typically the word "suspense" evokes images like a murderer hiding behind a door, or a bomb ready to explode. But suspense comes in many forms. If you were pulled over by the police because they thought you fit the description of a bank robber, but you thought you were being nailed for speeding, the tension leaps off the page.

You won't need to seed your story with close-calls and villainous surprises. Many situations can generate a sense of anticipation. For example, when you arrived at college, you had planned to study engineering. Then you go to your first fraternity party. Later that year, the night before a big exam instead of hitting the books you hit the bar. At each step, the reader feels growing tension between your desires and your actions, and wonders how it will be resolved.

Pay attention to suspense across the whole story, as well as in each chapter and scene. At each level, try to set up some sort of tension at the beginning that will be resolved by the end. To help you find themes for suspense:

- Keep in mind the central challenge of the story. Build suspense as you try to achieve this challenge.
- What is the character learning through the story? Build suspense as the character learns, or doesn't learn, the lesson.
- You can find a wealth of emotional tension inside your scenes. The characters' desires and fears let the reader feel the story's energy.
- Use storytelling devices to build suspense. For example, misunderstanding is the basis for tension in many dramas and comedies. When characters see things differently, from each other or from the audience, we feel tension until they resolve their differences. Comedies and dramas use impersonation to arouse suspense, as the audience worries about the exposure of the false identity.

Write

Pick a scene or chapter from your memoir. Try to frame the beginning of the scene in a way that sets up tension. By the end, you will resolve the tension. List a few steps that will let the reader gradually see this goal unfold.

25

Set up a challenge and then resolve it

In the first few minutes of the movie Rambo, the hero takes a break from chopping wood to look lovingly into his daughter's eyes. A few minutes later she's kidnapped. For the rest of the movie, we are willing to join Rambo on his quest, no matter how dangerous, murderous, or unlikely. We want him to save that girl. While the action movie has a big external event to capture our attention, every compelling story obeys this basic principle. Get the reader involved in the challenge. Then use that challenge to draw the reader to the end.

When we read genre books we have an idea about the challenge before we even look at the title. A mystery starts out with a crime, and we read because we want to see how it's solved. A romance starts out with a romantic challenge. A horror book introduces some assault on our sense of normalcy, and we want to see how the character handles it.

A memoir doesn't have this convenient built-in formula. It's up to you to invite the reader in. But before you can engage your reader in your story's central challenge, you need to understand it yourself. As you review the scenes and timeline of your story, look for patterns and strong emotions. From this material, find a central challenge that is strong enough to interest your readers and keep the story moving.

At first you may balk, thinking this is an artificial construction. "Who needs to invent a challenge? My life should speak for itself." But such an impulse to stick with the barren truth ignores the ancient requirements of storytelling. The teller provides a central idea to help the listener relate to the story. And once you find that idea, it will help you tell your story in a compelling way.

Unless you already have a completed storyline in mind, this search will be a creative one. It may appear immediately, but more likely you will see the general idea at first, and then continue to dig out your specific approach. For example, you want to write about the upheaval of your life in Vietnam. But what is the theme that carries the reader through? Do you want to tell about the challenge of coping with war, or coming of age, or the emotional struggles of falling in love, or finding and losing your best friend?

Write

Describe a challenge you want to write about. If you can think of more than one, imagine how these challenges might play out in the same book, or in more than one memoir.

Would these challenges grab your attention as a reader?

26

Write the cover copy

If the title of a book catches my eye, I flip it over to read the synopsis on the back. In a few sentences, I decide if I can relate to the story. The synopsis captures the essence of the world I'll enter when I read the book. Because of the power of the synopsis to capture so much about the book and fit it into so little space, you can use it in reverse. Instead of waiting until the book is complete, and then trying to describe what you've written, try writing the synopsis first.

By focusing on this tiny description, you will increase the clarity of your story. To write it, you will challenge yourself to define the main "engine" of the story. Will it be an "escape story?" A story of "redemption" or "coming of age?" These phrases may actually appear in the synopsis.

You'll soon find that it's hard to fit the essence of your life story into a paragraph or two. It may feel as if you're reducing yourself in some way. But that's exactly the value of the synopsis. It reminds you that you are not capturing your whole life. Rather you are trying to tell a story about it. And like any story, you need to organize your thinking in a way that will engage a reader. The synopsis doesn't diminish your life. It highlights the one story you are trying to tell.

Experiment with one theme and see how it works. Try another. Some themes may have the power to carry the whole story, while others may not fit at all. As you gather material, come back to this exercise and try again.

Review the emotions that fueled your scenes and the patterns that emerged in your timeline. Were you trying to please your dad or your uncle? Do you want to show how the upheaval in your native country profoundly affected your life? What power did you find in your coming of age story? Inside the book, you can weave several themes, but to write the synopsis, narrow it down to the central story question.

Research how other books accomplish this task. Take a few off your bookshelf and see how well their condensed message grabs your attention. Now imagine your own book. In fact, you don't have to imagine it. Print out a copy of your synopsis and tape it on the back of a book. Then as you are browsing through your shelf, pull that book out and read the back cover. Would it interest you enough to want to know more? You know you've succeeded when you can answer "yes."

Write

Write the back of the book as often as you would like to help you stay focused on a compelling storyline.

27

Embark on the Hero's Journey

The Hero's Journey is a story structure so universal that it looks like all humans are programmed to resonate with it. Take advantage of this programming by inserting your life story into the template of the Hero's Journey. Such a structure will offer your readers a familiar format reminiscent of tales they have been hearing since birth. In addition, its insights can help you understand where you've been and where you're going. Here are some of the broad strokes of the Hero's Journey to help you organize your story.

Prologue

Before the story starts, the hero lives within a familiar world. This initial world gives the reader a sense of the stability or normalcy the hero is going to leave behind.

Leave the familiar

The action of the story starts when the hero ventures out. Sometimes you left because you had to. You were evicted from a marriage, or a country. Or sometimes you leave because it's simply time to change, like when you reach adulthood or retirement. What "going forth" does your story start with? Did you quit, retire, or were you fired from your job? Did a chronic illness or financial downturn push you out of your familiar lifestyle?

Hear the call

After leaving the familiar world, the hero moves <u>toward</u> something, pulled in a particular direction by a mission. The message or idea that establishes this goal is known as the "Call." Luke Skywalker in Star Wars was given a specific message to save Princess Leah. The rest of us don't get such detailed instructions. To create your own Hero's Journey, look for the instructions you received. When did you know where you were heading, and how did you know it? The better you understand the Call, the better your reader will be able to relate to the story.

Write

What compelled you to move forward? Did you know about this goal from the beginning, or did you find out as you went along?

Face demons and obstacles

The most obvious thing about obstacles is that they hold you back. But in a deeper way, they actually force you to grow. Obstacles may be external, like lack of money or social support. Or they may be internal, like discouragement or fatigue. Your continuing effort to overcome these obstacles is one of the propelling forces of your story, and your life. Demons awaken the desire for survival and success.

Write

What obstacles did you face as moved toward a goal? What did you do to overcome them?

Hook up with allies -- create a micro-community

Your friends, mentors, teachers, and social network support you along your journey.

Write

List the people who helped you at various times in your life. How did they help?

Enter the "belly of the beast"

Deeper into your challenge, you realize there is no turning back. You enter the domain of the new world. Even though this domain is filled with terrors of the unknown, it also contains the seeds of new birth. After a horrible divorce, you find a new love. You were wounded in war, and find meaning in the work of peace. You lost your dreams, and over time, realize you have become an expert at understanding dreams.

Write

What part of your journey brought you face to face with seemingly impenetrable situations or questions?

Surviving the journey gives you wisdom

By entering the belly of the beast, you gain wisdom. You have faced challenges you didn't know you could overcome, and in overcoming them you have learned lessons and grown.

Write

What deeper lessons did you learn through your journey?

Returning home to share with your community

The end of the journey is a homecoming. Sometimes you really do come home, literally, for example, caring for and connecting with your aging parents. Sometimes the "home" is the community you created as an adult. In either case, you find a deeper meaning to your existence by sharing your strength with others.

Write

How is the place you return to different from the place you left? How is it the same?

Like the closing of a circle, you went forth and then came back. Your return will satisfy the reader that your journey has achieved an end. The homecoming contains the essence of the inner dimension of your story. When you return home, the protagonist sees the contrast between the beginning of the story and the end, and you realize how much your experience has taught you. The wisdom you earned on your journey is your offering to the community.

Write

What wisdom do you offer others as a "payment" for accepting you back, and as an offering to heal or help them?

28

Share your story with others

The goal of these lessons has been to help you create a story that can be appreciated by others. To complete your communication, you need an audience. Bring that daunting task within reach by reducing it to a series of gradual steps.

Fantasy audience

Create your first audience by imagining yourself telling your story to a few friends, whose rapt attention and occasional questions encourage you to open up, fill in the blanks, and tell them more. Your desire to tell and their desire to know create the perfect environment in which to shape your story.

Fellow writers

When you are ready, go beyond your imagined audience and look for people who share the desire to craft a story from life experience. Fellow memoir writers help each other by offering constructive feedback and support.

Extended family

The obvious audience for many memoirists are kids and grandkids. But why stop there? Send a newsletter to cousins. Ask them for their recollections. Find other relatives who are interested in family history and join forces.

Special interest groups

Are you a recovering alcoholic and have a story that might help other people overcome their addiction? If so, you have a special interest audience. The same holds true if you are a hospice worker, a survivor of a war, or have a compelling tale about any other special interest. Tell your story to members of organizations that have reason to be interested in your tale.

Commercial publications

While much of the money for memoirs goes to celebrities, politicians, and other people in the public eye, there is always a market for well-told tales. But to find a place in commercial publication, you will need to learn the ropes of the business. I suggest you use the goal of commercial publication to your advantage. Instead of shying away because of the need for salesmanship and business acumen, dangle it in front of yourself like a carrot to keep you moving toward an ever improved story.

New technology broadens your opportunities

With the explosion of technology has come a vast range of choices for letting other people access your writing, from your own website to online magazines, videos, blogs, podcasts, ebooks, wikis, and print on demand books. Every month or two a new form enables us to share ideas. This explosion of technologies follows naturally from the power we humans have to tell and hear stories.

Write

Who will you reach with your story?

How will you reach them?

Keep going

By the time I was 21, I knew quite a bit about who I already was and who I was setting out to be. But despite my sense of certainty, things kept changing. Sometimes I made progress more slowly than I expected. At other times, my path veered off in a direction I had not anticipated. In some years I aspired to goals I didn't even know about the year before. Now when I look back at my life and try to tell my story, I discover that the way it all turned out was nothing like what I expected. Probably the most surprising thing of all was that the whole thing went on for so darn long.

I had no excuse for surprise — our culture abounds with warnings about how long journeys can take. For example, in the Bible, after the Israelis were set free, it took them forty years in the desert before they arrived at their destination. In Homer's Odyssey, when Ulysses triumphantly left the battlefield, it took him seven years to reach home. I knew these stories, but I didn't apply them to myself.

In the enthusiasm of youth, everything is within reach. Then gradually, the sheer length of life becomes apparent. Growing up—raising kids—building a career—growing old—it all takes time.

Similarly, writing a memoir is a journey. Find the facts and organize them. Write the scenes. With practice, your skills improve. Writing a memoir is not just about past events. It's also a creative journey that you are embarking on today.

As you have done so many times before, you will adapt to the length of this journey, adjusting to ups and downs along the way. To keep going, use the life skills you have learned. Practice. Persist. Occasionally look back and savor signs of progress. Recruit allies in memoir and writing groups. When you gain confidence, polish an article and email it to family members. Publish it in a newsletter or post it on a website.

Find the other side of life

Writing is a complex blend of skills, combining artistry, communication, a sense of emotional connection, and liveliness. Finding, crafting, and wordsmithing stories turns out to be a never ending challenge that brings with it enormous rewards. The craft of writing can keep you excited and connected with people for the rest of your life.

By sharing your story with others, you might solve the puzzle Joni Mitchell posed when she asked us how to find the meaning of life in just two sides. Perhaps the two sides she was searching for are the two stories that bind each of us – the story of me and the story of you. By offering our stories to one another, like two sides of a coin, we create a whole.

Notes

Notes

Notes

Jerry Waxler

Jerry Waxler, M.S., is a speaker, writing coach, and therapist. His workshops "How to get started" and "How to keep going" resulted in the "Four Elements for Writers," a self-development book for writers who want to overcome obstacles. For more information about his books, workshops, and other events and to sign up for his mailing list, visit www.jerrywaxler.com or email Jerry at jerrywaxler@yahoo.com.